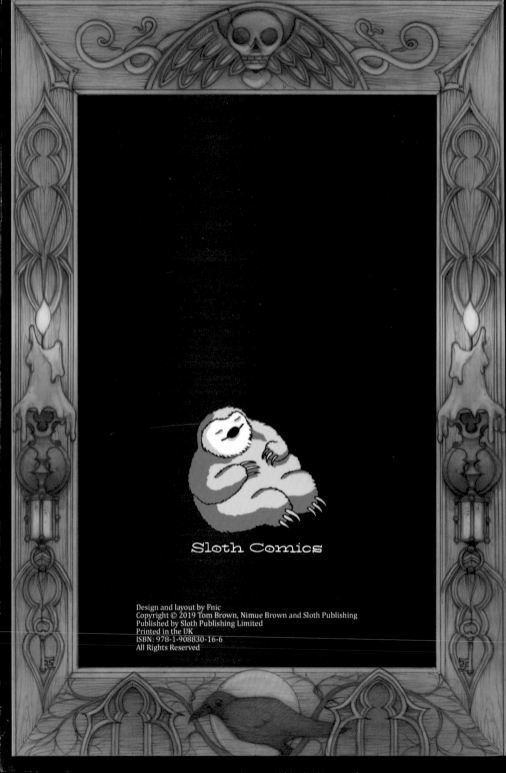

Sloth Comics

Design and layout by Fnic
Copyright © 2019 Tom Brown, Nimue Brown and Sloth Publishing
Published by Sloth Publishing Limited
Printed in the UK
ISBN: 978-1-908830-16-6
All Rights Reserved

Dedication

This volume of Hopeless, Maine is dedicated to Nicolas Rossert.

Nick is our editor, publisher, and friend and this book would not be in your hands right now if it were not for him. I'll go further. There is a very good chance that there would be no continuing Hopeless, Maine in published form if it were not for Nick. His faith in our work and his commitment to this series have kept us going when things seemed..well, hopeless. His professionalism, fairness, and kindness have made it an absolute pleasure to continue in our work. Nick looks out for the creators he publishes and the creators under the sloth umbrella (erm) have come to feel very much like family because of this. So, thank you for putting up with us and sending us out into the wide world in book form, sir!

He is so long-suffering that he did not even complain when I turned him into a were-sloth!

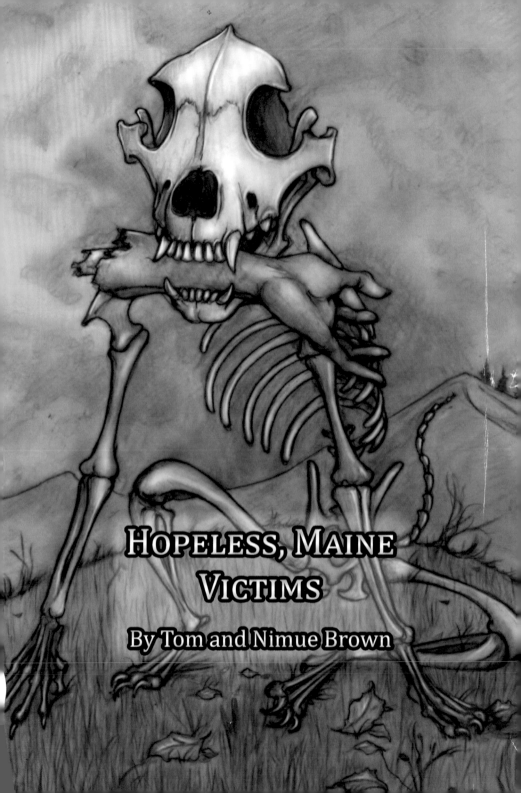

Hopeless, Maine
Victims

By Tom and Nimue Brown

CHAPTER ONE

"Just call me Red Riding Hood."

Welcome to my island.
A small, desolate place but nonetheless, I like to think of it as home. It may surprise you that one such as myself can find amusement in these limited conditions. Call it a gift, if you will. A talent. Those who do not breathe and do not die, and yet cough. Those who have died, and are unable to rest. All their petty fears and jealousies I paint large for them. I am generous in this way. It gives a little colour and meaning to their otherwise empty lives. How could they not adore me?

CHAPTER TWO

"I see you, whatever you are."

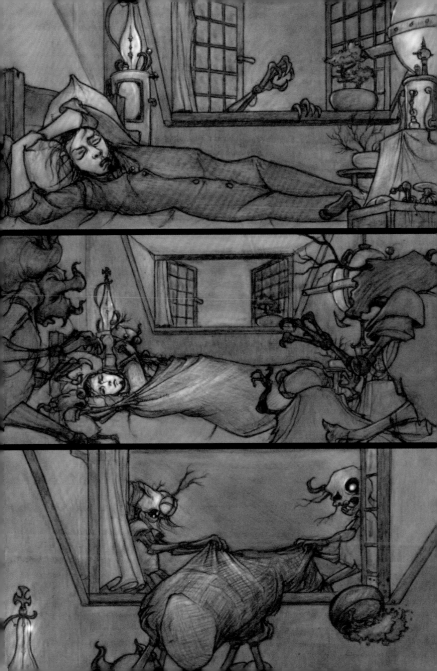

CHAPTER THREE

"You're dead in all the
ways that really matter."

CHAPTER FOUR

"I used to think the moon
was a massive biscuit."

YOU KNOW, MY USUAL IDEA OF A PARTY INVOLVES A FEW GLASSES OF WINE, BITS OF CHEESE ON PEELED TWIGS, SOMEONE SINGING A FEW SONGS. COLD, DAMP TUNNELS NEVER CROSSED MY MIND BEFORE.

SOUNDS LIKE WE'VE FOUND THE PARTY.

WHERE DID YOUR LIGHT GO?

I DON'T KNOW.

WELCOME OWEN DAVIES, GOBLIN KING. WELCOME SALAMANDRA O'STOAT, SORCERESS.

HELLO. CAN WE HAVE SOME LIGHT? I'D MUCH RATHER SEE WHO I'M TALKING TO.

BY ALL MEANS. THE LIGHT IS NO ENEMY TO US...

...NOR IS THE DARKNESS.

CHAPTER FIVE

"It's amazing how long a person can live for after you've peeled their skin off.

"Nothing will kill them all like face to face."

IN MY HANDS, IT IS HARD TO TELL THE DIFFERENCE BETWEEN MINUTES AND HOURS.

OWEN!
BEHIND YOU!

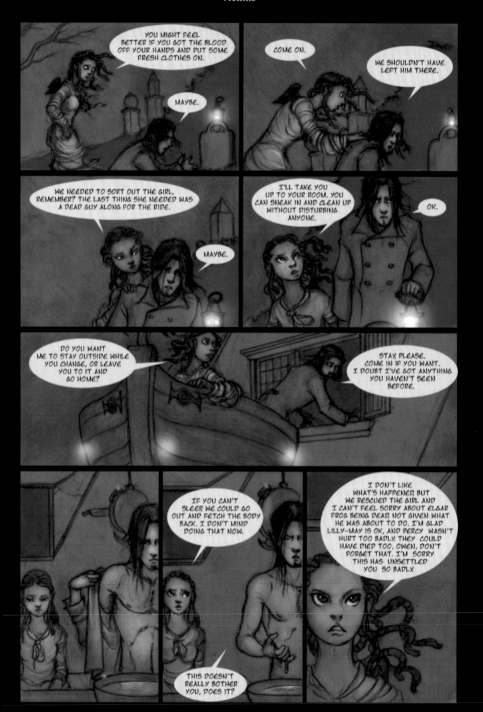

"The Fog is not beautiful."

I LIKE FIRELIGHT. IT'S SO FRIENDLY. I LIKE THE WAY IT SOFTENS EVERYTHING. IN HERE, WITH THE CURTAINS DRAWN, AND THE FIRE, YOU CAN ALMOST FORGET EVERYTHING ELSE. I TRY TO, ANYWAY.

WHAT DO YOU THINK IT WOULD BE LIKE HERE, WITHOUT THE FOG?

I DON'T KNOW. WHAT WAS IT LIKE WHERE YOU WENT?

ODD, BUT IN DIFFERENT WAYS. NOT KNOWING ANYONE WAS SCARY FOR A START. BUT THERE WAS SUNLIGHT MOST DAYS, REAL WARM-ON-YOUR-SKIN SUNLIGHT, AND THE FOOD — THERE WAS SO MUCH OF IT, AND IT WAS SO GOOD. THE TECHNOLOGY, AND THE CITIES. I SAW SO MUCH. IT'S LIKE WE'RE TRAPPED IN THE PAST HERE. THE REST OF THE WORLD IS MOVING APACE, AND WE'RE TRAPPED IN THE FOG.

YOU COULD HAVE ROAMED THE WORLD, BUT YOU CAME BACK.

OF COURSE I DID.

NOT EVERYONE WOULD HAVE DONE.

MAYBE NOT. ALL THE TIME I WAS OUT THERE, THINKING HOW DIFFERENT IT WAS FROM HERE. I JUST WANTED TO COME BACK AND PUT THINGS RIGHT.

SEE, YOU'RE JUST NATURALLY HEROIC. YOU ALWAYS USED TO RESCUE ME FROM YOUR FATHER.

OR RESCUE MY FATHER FROM YOU. I WAS NEVER ENTIRELY SURE WHICH WAY ROUND THAT WAS. I THINK YOU FRIGHTEN HIM.

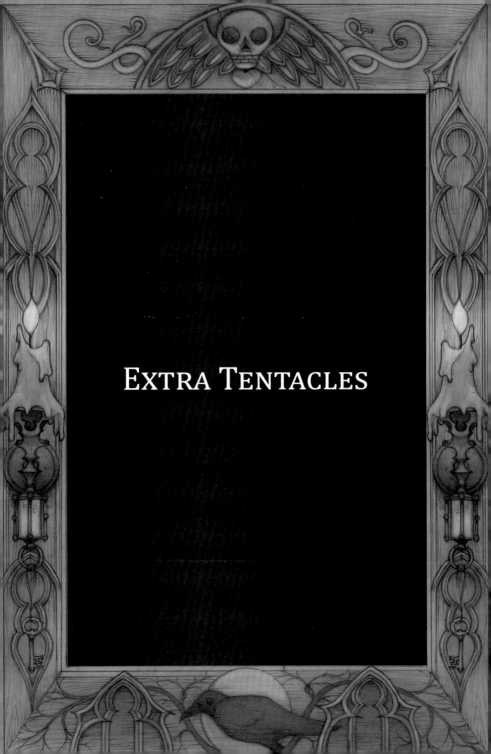

EXTRA TENTACLES

~ Doctor Willoughby kept the best remedies for himself ~

By,Seb Burnett, the creator of the Bertram Fiddle
games-www.bertramfiddle.com

Starry-Grabby Pie

More fool the naïve diner who orders this tentacled treat from
Pieney Todd's Elaborate Pastry Emporium. Fresh from the oven, the
alluring brown crust soon reveals that the wriggling 'matter' has not
only completely survived the archaic cooking process, but also now
seems dangerously infuriated by it. Hiding all nearby cutlery,
immediately paying the exorbitant bill and backing away very slowly
are recommended.

Phil and Jacqui Lovesey-www.matlockthehare.com

The original character design for Percy
Art by Tom Brown

Poor Ms Lovelace used to be a travel writer until tl
wreck. Now she finds herself in a strange world kno·
··ess, Maine, with strange powers bestowed upon her |
new "patron", Ctholin...
Art and words by Francesca Dare-
http://www.pennyblackfeather.co.uk/blog/